嫦娥

Chang'e's Ascent to the Moon

传说远古的时候，天上忽然出现了十个太阳，不分昼夜地发光发热，直烤得海水干枯，土地干裂，生灵涂炭。天神后羿为民除害射下了九个太阳，只留下一个太阳白天出来，晚上落下，用光和热温暖着大地。

这十个太阳都是天帝的儿子，天帝一怒之下把后羿贬为凡人。人们把后羿当作英雄崇拜，很多人都来拜师学艺，他每日里狩猎、传授武艺，对人间的生活也很适应。

According to legend, one day ten suns suddenly arose together in the sky, blazing over the earth. As a result, the sea dried up, the land was scorched and the people were plunged into an abyss of misery. Houyi, a celestial archer, descended from heaven to rescue the people on earth and shot down nine of the ten suns. The last surviving sun was terrified; since then, every day the sun has risen at dawn in the east and set at dusk in the west, fulfilling its duty by illuminating the whole earth.

The ten suns were the children of the God of Heaven, who was very annoyed with Houyi for his shooting down nine of them to save the earth. As punishment, the God of Heaven banished Houyi and his wife Chang'e to live as mere mortals on earth. People worshiped Houyi as a hero, and many came to train with him. Hunting wild animals and teaching archery skills every day, Houyi adjusted well to his life as a mortal.

后羿的妻子嫦娥，是天宫里有名的美人。她容貌俏丽，身姿婀娜。当她随着音乐翩翩起舞的时候，没有人不为她着迷。嫦娥随后羿被贬到人间之后，两人朝夕相伴，度过了一段美好时光。

一天晚上，盛大的篝火晚会正在举行。嫦娥挥舞长袖载歌载舞，可是当她想像从前那样飞到半空的时候，却忽然发现自己飞不起来了。一丝惆怅涌上了她的心头，她终于明白自己已经不再是神仙了。

Chang'e was a beautiful young girl who had worked in the Heavenly Palace. Everyone had been captivated by her charm whenever she began dancing to music. After being banished to the earth, she and Houyi had lived together happily, enjoying a beautiful time together.

One evening, at a grand campfire party, Chang'e danced lightly, gracefully waving the long sleeves of her dress, but when she tried to float up in the air as she had been used to doing, she suddenly found that she had lost the ability. A feeling of sadness welled up in her heart as she realized that she was no longer an immortal.

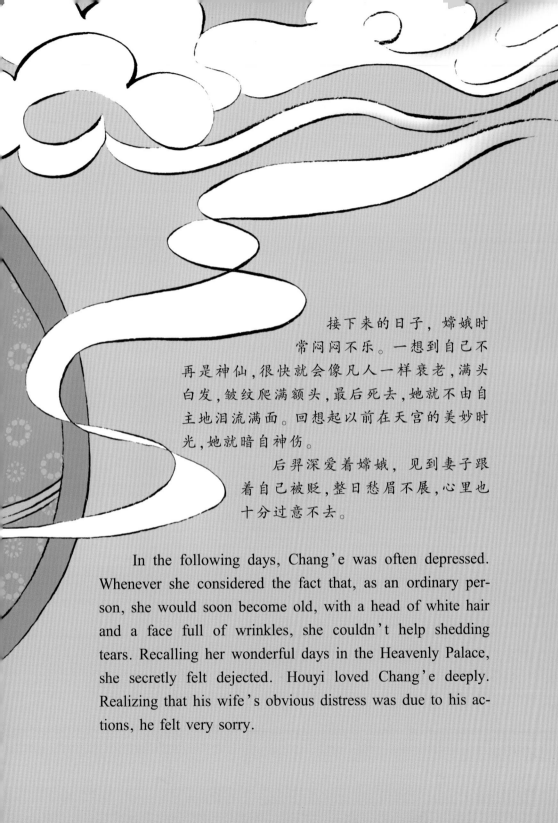

接下来的日子，嫦娥时常闷闷不乐。一想到自己不再是神仙，很快就会像凡人一样衰老，满头白发，皱纹爬满额头，最后死去，她就不由自主地泪流满面。回想起以前在天宫的美妙时光，她就暗自神伤。

后羿深爱着嫦娥，见到妻子跟着自己被贬，整日愁眉不展，心里也十分过意不去。

In the following days, Chang'e was often depressed. Whenever she considered the fact that, as an ordinary person, she would soon become old, with a head of white hair and a face full of wrinkles, she couldn't help shedding tears. Recalling her wonderful days in the Heavenly Palace, she secretly felt dejected. Houyi loved Chang'e deeply. Realizing that his wife's obvious distress was due to his actions, he felt very sorry.

一天，后羿听说昆仑山上西王母那里有一种不死灵药，于是他下定决心要找来送给嫦娥。他辞别嫦娥，走过了九百九十九座山，趟过了九百九十九条河，日夜兼程历经千辛万苦，终于爬上了昆仑山，找到了西王母。

One day, Houyi heard that the Queen Mother of the West, who lived in the Kunlun Mountains, had a magic elixir, so he made up his mind to seek it out for Chang'e. Saying goodbye to his beloved wife, he climbed over nine-hundred-and-ninety-nine mountains, crossed nine-hundred-and- ninety-nine rivers, pressing on with his journey day and night. After untold hardships, he finally climbed up the Kunlun Mountains and met the Queen Mother of the West.

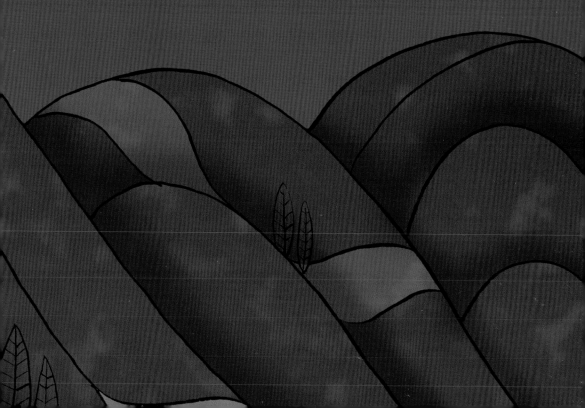

西王母早就听说过后羿射日为民除害反而被贬的事，对他十分赞赏和同情。

得知后羿的来意后，西王母拿出两粒药来，说道："这灵药是从不死树上采下的果子经过提炼之后制成的。不死树三千年开一次花，三千年结一次果，三千年才成熟。所以，灵药非常稀少。你把它拿回去，吃一粒长生不老，吃两粒即刻就可以升天。"

The Queen Mother of the West had long ago heard the story of how Houyi had been banished from the heavens for ridding the people of an evil. She admired and sympathized with him deeply.

Knowing his purpose in coming, the Queen Mother of the West agreed to give him the panacea and said, "This elixir came from the fruit picked from a tree of immortality which takes three thousand years to blossom, three thousand years to fruit, and three thousand years to mature, so, it is a rare and magical preparation. One pill will make you immortal; two pills will make you float into the sky at once."

　　后羿舍不得丢下心爱的妻子一个人成仙，就把灵药拿回来交给嫦娥。两人商量择个吉时一起服用灵药，这样就可以长生不老、相伴终生。嫦娥小心地把灵药收起来，放进梳妆台的百宝匣里。

　　没想到，他们的谈话被后羿的一个名叫蓬蒙的徒弟听到了，这个人心术不正，顿时起了歹意。

Houyi was loath to part with his beloved wife to go back to heaven by himself. He brought the elixer home and asked Chang'e to store it to be used later. The couple decided to pick a lucky day to take the pills together so that they could become immortals again.

Unfortunately, they were unaware that they had been overheard by Peng Meng, one of Houyi's pupils. He was a calculating person, and he quickly formulated a malicious plan.

这一天，正逢农历八月十五。后羿带着徒弟们进山狩猎，蓬蒙假装生病留在家中。后羿刚一离开，他就来到嫦娥的房间，持刀威逼她交出灵药。嫦娥知道自己不是蓬蒙的对手，情急之下她转身打开百宝匣，拿出不死药一口吞了下去。

On that day, which happened to be the fifteenth day of the eighth lunar month, Houyi led his pupils to a mountain to hunt wild animals while Peng Meng, feigning illness, stayed at home. As soon as Houyi left, Peng Meng came into Cheng'e's room with a dagger in his hand and forced her to hand over the elixer. Knowing that she was no match for him, Chang'e suddenly turned around, opened the case, took out the pills and swallowed them down.

嫦娥吃下灵药,只觉得身体越来越轻,脚离开地面,缓缓向天上飞去。尽管心中对后羿有无限的留恋,可她想停也停不下来,就这样飞出窗口,升天而去。到了离地球最近的月亮,嫦娥住了下来,成了一个月宫仙子。

Then Chang'e, feeling her body become lighter and lighter, slowly started to float into the sky. Although her heart broke at the prospect of parting from Houyi, she had no choice but to fly out of the window and up. She finally landed on the moon where she became a Moon Fairy.

后羿回来后，知道了事情原委，愤怒地去找蓬蒙算账。可这家伙早已溜走了。后羿悲痛欲绝，仰望着夜空思念心爱的妻子。隔着遥远的距离，他望见皎洁的月亮里仿佛有一个熟悉的身影，那正是自己心爱的妻子。

After coming back, Houyi found what had happened and angrily went to look for Peng Meng, but he had already slipped away. Houyi's heart ached as he looked up at the night sky, longing to see his wife. Gazing across the vast distance, he saw in the bright and clear moon what seemed to be a familiar figure, the form of his beloved Chang'e.

后羿急忙派人到后花园里摆上香案，放上嫦娥平时喜欢吃的水果蜜饯，遥祭妻子。百姓听说嫦娥成仙的事情后，也学着后羿的样子，纷纷摆上香案水果，向月宫仙子祈求幸福平安。八月十五拜月的风俗就这样传了下来，成了中秋节。

Houyi hurriedly directed people to set up an altar in the backyard with incense and some fruit so that he could worship his wife from afar. After the news spread that Chang'e had become a Moon Fairy, people everywhere set up alters with incense and fruit to pray to the Moon Fairy for happiness and peace. The custom of worshiping the moon on the fifteenth day of the eighth lunar month was passed down and later developed into the Mid-autumn Festival.

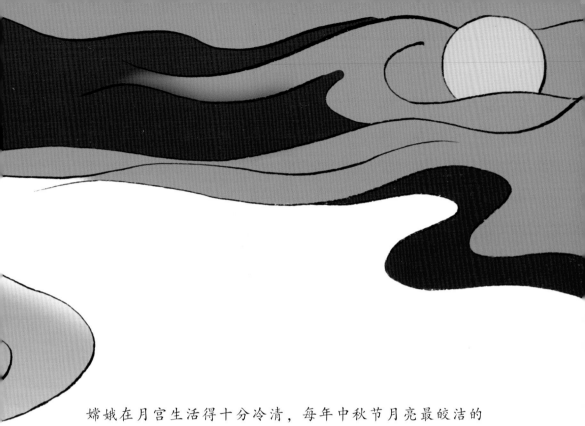

嫦娥在月宫生活得十分冷清，每年中秋节月亮最皎洁的时候,她都会回忆自己从前的幸福生活。

月母为后羿和嫦娥的真情所感动，于是允许嫦娥每年农历八月十五下凡与后羿在月桂树下相会。

Chang'e became lonely in the Lunar Palace without her husband, so every year, during the Mid-autumn Festival when the moon was full and bright, she would recall her past happy life.

The Moon Lady was touched by the story of Houyi and Chang'e, so she allowed Chang'e to meet Houyi beneath a laurel tree on the fifteenth day of the eighth lunar month every year.

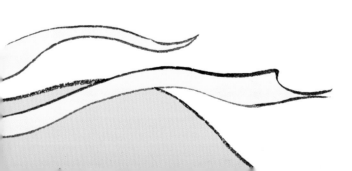

完

End